Hampshire & Wiltshire

Edited By Donna Samworth

First published in Great Britain in 2019 by:

Young**Writers**®
—— Est. 1991 ——

Young Writers
Remus House
Coltsfoot Drive
Peterborough
PE2 9BF
Telephone: 01733 890066
Website: www.youngwriters.co.uk

FOREWORD

Here at Young Writers, we love to let imaginations run wild and creativity go crazy. Our aim is to encourage young people to get their creative juices flowing and put pen to paper. Each competition is tailored to the relevant age group, hopefully giving each pupil the inspiration and incentive to create their own piece of creative writing, whether it's a poem or a short story. By allowing them to see their own work in print, we know their confidence and love for the written word will grow.

For our latest competition Poetry Wonderland, we invited primary school pupils to create wild and wonderful poems on any topic they liked – the only limits were the limits of their imagination! Using poetry as their magic wand, these young poets have conjured up worlds, creatures and situations that will amaze and astound or scare and startle! Using a variety of poetic forms of their own choosing, they have allowed us to get a glimpse into their vivid imaginations. We hope you enjoy wandering through the wonders of this book as much as we have.

CONTENTS

Megan Costello (10)   70

Medina Primary School, Cosham

Hope Blossom Morgan-Hilliar (9)   71
Oliver Stagg (8)   72
Farin Salehabadi (8)   73
Edward Patrick Simmons (9)   74
Jacey Bamba (9)   75
Lola Wilbur (9)   76
Gracie Walters (9)   77

Red Oaks Primary School, Swindon

Maanya Sekhar (11)   78
Emily Norris (11)   80
Sami Khan (11)   81

St Barnabas Primary School, Market Lavington

Eliza Bates (11)   82
Jamie Saunders (10)   83
Maisie Ann Rodger (11)   84
Ruby McLellan (10)   85
Mollie Rodger (9)   86
Isabel Josse Chammings (9)   87
Matilda Sharp (10)   88
Cameron Maxwell (11)   89
Toby Morgan (10)   90
Jake Dyer (11)   91
Isla Mughal (10)   92
Charlie Ottaway (9)   93
Katie Swanborough (11)   94
Harley James Williams (10)   95
Katie Stabbins (11)   96
Millie Winstanley (9)   97
Ben Smith (10)   98

St Catherine's Catholic Primary School, Stratton

Elsie Lowrie (8)   99
Atkins Tofilo Msury (9)   100
Elyanna Jackson (8)   102
Oliver Truchanowicz (9)   103
Conall McFarnon (8)   104
Juan Andres Guanchez (8)   105
Maimie Belcher (8)   106
Eleanor Davis (8)   107
Victoria Skoczek (8)   108
Elsie Anello (9)   109
Jack Parker (8)   110
Joseph Szymon Mobey (8)   111
Archie Leddy (9)   112
Maja Skowron (9)   113
Jan Graz (8)   114
Ciaran Hamilton (9)   115
Amelia Kunz (9)   116
Gavin Chen (9)   117
Zac Smith (9)   118
Florence Zajt (9)   119
Leah Antionette Quinn (9)   120
Sienna Meade (8)   121
Wiktoria Wozniak (9)   122
Austin Geoff Jones (9)   123
Harley Gwazeni (9)   124

St John's CE Primary School, Tisbury

Sandy Evans (10)   125
Maisie Burt (11)   126
Grace Major (10)   127

St Mark's CE Junior School, Salisbury

Mya Sales (9)   128
Carla Carpenter-Paya (9)   129
Annabel Robyn Leonie   130
Arnold (9)
Izzie Davies-Evans (9)   132
Nyah Rose Gordon (10)   133

Kaci-May Dempsey (7)	134
Holly Leeming (9)	135
Nancy Neville (8)	136
Tilde Williams (8)	137
Sophie Lee (8)	138
Enya Harding (8)	139
Joey Larkham (7)	140

Western CE Primary School, Winchester

Joseph Ager (10)	141

Whitesheet Primary Academy, Zeals

Charlotte Higgins (9)	142
Elliot Winter-White (7)	143
Nathaniel Winter-White (9)	144
Ellie-May Manning (8)	145
Fae Duggan (8)	146
Stefan Pirvulescu (8)	147
Summer Johnson (10)	148
Albert Antony Ransome (8)	149
Elliot Hayes (8)	150

Wickham CE Primary School, Wickham

Katie Vollentine (9)	151
Summer Mullins (8)	152
Poppy Lock (8)	154
Libby-Rose Fitzgerald (9)	155

Wylye Valley CEVA Primary School, Codford

Oliver Barnes (10)	156
Poppy Barnes (10)	157
Margot Clarke (10)	158

★ The Poems ★

Gran's Christmas Tree

It's spring and the air is full of love,
But my mum went crazy and my dad had enough,
This is all 'cause of typical Nanny,
Bet you'll be guessing what she's done now,
She went haywire on the roof,
She's decided to keep her Christmas tree until
June.

Gran's Christmas tree,
Gran's Christmas tree,
Why are you here?
All I can hear are your mini Santas,
All I can see are your wavy antlers,
It's blocking the TV and I can't hear a thing!

Gran's Christmas tree,
Gran's Christmas tree,
Why are you here?
All I can hear are your mini Santas,
All I can see are your wavy antlers,
It's blocking the TV and I can't hear a thing!

Tsion Mhari (10)
Corpus Christi RC (A) Primary School, Portsmouth

Falling Down A Rabbit Hole

Walking in the forest,
With a skip in my step,
Thinking about a dream,
A dream I'll never forget.

All of a sudden,
I took an almighty slip
Down a rabbit hole,
Oh, boy, did I trip!

Oh my goodness,
I couldn't believe my eyes,
There was a rabbit
Eating French fries!

Then I spied two boys
With fat tums,
I heard the rabbit say,
"Oi! Tweedledee and Tweedledum!"

Oh, the Mad Hatter,
The Mad Hatter you say,
He is crazy
In every way.

He invited me to his tea party,
It was so cool
But the crazy rabbit himself
Was playing the fool.

Every time the Mad Hatter spoke,
Out came the funniest joke,
But now I'm sad that I have to go,
Will I see them again? Nobody will know!

Daisy Broad (10)
Corpus Christi RC (A) Primary School, Portsmouth

The Dream Of Promises

Can't wait to sleep,
Can't wait to dream.
Take me away,
I hate this place, accept me please,
Into a world of happiness
There is a lot for me to see,
I really would love a beautiful dream,
Where I can stay and I can live
Instead of this orphanage,
I'm going, I'm drifting,
I'm going way up in the air,
The clouds, here, there,
I'm about to fall on the fluffiest one of all,
Pretty girls with lots of pearls
Jumping high into the sky,
Giggling, wiggling, jumping,
Thumping, racing, running and hopping,
The fluffy and puffy clouds
As soft as marshmallows,
Warm, cosy and rosy I feel,
Oh, how I would like to stay here for real,

Imagine forever in my dreams,
Maybe one day I will.

Milo Keating (10)
Corpus Christi RC (A) Primary School, Portsmouth

My Dragon

I have a dragon for a pet,
Oh, yes a dragon you can bet,
It is nocturnal, it sleeps all day
And comes out in the night to play.

I like to ride on its back,
However, quietness it does lack,
From its tummy will come a roar,
It'll make you say, "Oh no! No more!"

He has large wings, as red as blood,
He likes to roll around in mud,
He loves to make a mess so big
And eats a lot, just like a pig.

He has vast green eyes,
As big as pies,
His favourite snacks are cheese and eggs,
When he farts, I need nose pegs.

Esmé Elizabeth Quinton (10)
Corpus Christi RC (A) Primary School, Portsmouth

We're Not What He Says!

They can all stare,
But I will never care,
I know I eat strangely,
But at least I do it quickly.

I am aware of how I look,
But at least I don't stare like you,
I know what you are,
But it's not good you look like an octopus,
I mean, you have the look,
But you don't have the talent
Or happiness.

No one will be surprised when I say
That you and I are not what we say,
You can keep staring but I will say,
"Hey, everyone, we are a type of alien!"

Anna Idiata-Mendez (11)
Corpus Christi RC (A) Primary School, Portsmouth

Down And Down The Rabbit Hole

Down and down the rabbit hole,
You never know where you'll halt,
You stop and have a quick tea with a bunny,
You then bolt off,
Now, you're starting to cough
Due to the steamy conditions,
You switch off,
Relaxing to the soft, classical music flooding your ears,
Are you there yet?
No, you bet?
Where were you heading?
Halt!
Now you're there!
Interesting smells burst in your nose,
Loud festival music penetrating your thudding ears,
Could you be at...
Wonderland?

Grace Heather (10)

Corpus Christi RC (A) Primary School, Portsmouth

The Gorilla And The Grape

The gorilla ate a grape,
He decided that it was not the right shape.
In order to correct its appearance,
The gorilla needed some assistance.
He called over the leopard
Who looked rather pressured,
For he knew there was a grape,
That was a very funny shape
In the gut or the butt of this very hairy ape.
The very pressured leopard
Called over the hyperactive shepherd,
Who performed a radioactive test
And they all tried their best,
To remove the grape
That was a very funny shape!

Jaydon Patrick Broomhead (11)
Corpus Christi RC (A) Primary School, Portsmouth

Things I Love Most

I see Lego bricks falling
Straight out of the sky,
I'm floating around
To figure out why.

Where have they come from?
Why do they fall?
It doesn't make any sense at all.

I have a crazy idea,
I don't know if it will work,
I will take my golf clubs
And take back my space.

I hit brick after brick after brick,
Until there is no more,
Now nothing is falling,
No bricks to be seen,
Just me and my scooter,
Now that was a fun dream!

Jamie Ellis Duke (9)
Corpus Christi RC (A) Primary School, Portsmouth

The Unknown

I know you're scared of the unknown,
You sure don't wanna be alone,
Your shadows are your only, lonely company.

Mysterious fog and arthritic branches
Chase you through the chaos
Of this nightmare.

Emerging from the mist,
As your veins tighten within your fists.

Your heart is in your mouth,
But the beating is in your head,
You think you may be dead!

No...

You're in the panic room!

Kit Mackenzie (11)
Corpus Christi RC (A) Primary School, Portsmouth

Little Red Panda

Little red panda is swinging in a tree,
He's young and soft, he's completely free,
Bamboo is what he likes to eat,
So he waddles through the grass on his little furry feet,
Soft little ears and a little button nose,
Two bright eyes and fuzzy little toes,
He hops around in the canopy,
Paradise and freedom is all he can see,
As the moon sets on high wooden trees,
Little red panda falls asleep to the cool summer breeze.

Joe Gofton (10)
Corpus Christi RC (A) Primary School, Portsmouth

If My Dog Could Talk

If my dog could talk, what would she say?
"Can you take me for a walk on this bright sunny
day?
I'm bored with this dog meat,
Give me some ham,
A spag bol, lasagne
Or toast with jam.

I've slept in your bed all day long,
Even though I know it's wrong,
I love to chew my favourite toy,
It passes the time of day!"
If my dog could talk,
That's what I think she'd say.

Hollie Louise Davis (11)

Corpus Christi RC (A) Primary School, Portsmouth

A Roller Coaster Round The Sun

Up and out of the atmosphere
Makes the stars quite clear,
I thought this would be fun,
I got burnt by the sun,
Spinning around the hottest thing ever
Makes me want to shout and cry,
Five minutes up and five minutes down doesn't make it seem long,
But trust me, it is not fast when you're there,
When I got down,
All I had was spiky hair and a burnt face.

Lucas Jennison (9)
Corpus Christi RC (A) Primary School, Portsmouth

My Alien Friend

Boom! Pop! Bang!
It all happened in a blank
And you needed to go back,
So I needed to think of a plan.

You asked me many questions,
Which put me into confusion,
You needed to get prepared,
But you didn't really care.

One, two, three,
You call out that you're ready,
Four, five, six,
Let's meet again.

Fia Shaji (9)
Corpus Christi RC (A) Primary School, Portsmouth

The Rainbow Roller Coaster

On a sunny day, high in the sky,
I take my seat, ready to fly,
In my seat, blasting up into the cloud,
Everyone could hear me scream so loud.
I reached the top, there's only one way down
As I shoot back to the ground.
As my head is spinning,
I feel like I'm winning,
Other kids are in school,
I feel like I rule.

Keelan Sayin (10)
Corpus Christi RC (A) Primary School, Portsmouth

The World Of Endings

Many things have endings,
Like books, films and more,
Some endings will be dramatic,
Others you will adore.

Go deep into the world of endings
And be a scuba diver,
Or you could simply whizz through it,
Like a racing driver.

For Dorothy, she went to see Oz,
So she could go home at last,
With the scarecrow and all her new friends
She got there very fast.

There's an example of an ending,
That ended fairly well,
But not all are so magical,
For the big bad wolf, he experienced Hell.

Amelia Fisher (11)
Fynamore Primary School, Calne

The Stone Of Evil

I'm sure we've all heard of the fairies and elves
And poured over the tales of wonder on our shelves,
I'm sure we've heard all the tales of old
Of magic and fantasy and heroes bold.

But, amidst all that sparkle,
Beneath all that glitz,
There is a stone of dark magic
No evil figure could resist.

I speak a word of warning,
I've come to help prepare
Poor Fairyland, the beautiful woods
For the evil waiting there.

Is Fairyland in danger?
I fear it is, for
Bad things have been happening
And I'm sure there will be more.

Meanwhile, the fairies were panicking,
The elves and pixies too,

They didn't see what was going on,
They were planning what to do.

Evil spirits rise!
Have evil spirits risen?
Now all step forward, go ahead
And say we'll never get put in prison!

The spirits glide off,
But the fairies have all stood,
"Charge!" yells a pixie,
"Let's bombard them with our good!"

Paige Wood (11)
Fynamore Primary School, Calne

The Elf Who Came To Tea

Yesterday, I met an elf.
His name was Micky Trotter.
I found him very pleasant
And invited him to tea.

He guzzled down the biscuits.
He slurped up all the milk.
He danced upon the tablecloth.
Don't invite elves to tea!

He shook up all the lemonade.
He juggled all my bonbons.
He stamped and stomped and waved his hands.
Don't invite elves to tea!

He stuck pancakes on the ceiling.
He put noodles in my hair.
He threw away my chocolate cake.
Don't invite elves to tea!

By then, he was quite tired
So I shooed him out of the house.

He begged and begged to come back in.
I think he's still there now!

Alana Wells (10)

Fynamore Primary School, Calne

The Monsters Of The Night

Have you ever wondered
What happens in the night
When you are asleep,
That could wake you with a fright?

The first one is the Blooddrinker,
A stealthy monster he is,
Swimming in the blood of the river
A deadly monster he is.

The next one is the Bloodbottler,
With that gruesome look of his,
He sucks the blood of his enemies
And his hair is green with frizz.

May this be your warning
Of the horrors of the night,
For more can come,
If you're not careful, they might!

Zoe Trueman (10)
Fynamore Primary School, Calne

Embarrassing Things

My name is Sury Lee
And I'm about to tell you
Embarrassing things that happened to me.

I left the toilet seat
With tissue on my feet.
I was playing the drums
And lost track of the beat.
I read my book upside down
And everyone said, "What a clown!"
I went to the shop and everyone looked at me
Because I only had one little penny.

They're embarrassing things that happened to me,
But usually, people laugh and that makes me full
of glee!

Ruby Fisher (11)
Fynamore Primary School, Calne

Candy Land Invaded By Monsters

Candy! Candy! Everywhere,
Candy! Candy! What a fair,
Monsters munching on a Wispa,
Monsters scrunching on the candy,
Save our candy! Save it!
Monsters crunching on the sweets,
Oh no! They have got the sweets!
Oh no! They have got the candy!
Monsters are bad business,
Monsters are taking over the rainbow,
Now, where can unicorns jump without their
unicorn colours?
Monsters! Monsters! Oh no!
Invaded! Invaded! By monsters!

That's why you keep your candy safe,
Otherwise the crunching, munching, scrunching
monsters
Will eat it all up!

Florence Bridges (7)
Grateley Primary School, Grateley

Tasteless Tacos

"What can I have on tacos, Mum?"

"Well, you can have...

Apple strudel
Or poodles,
Or a goat on a boat,
Or a bit of toast on a float,
Or a cat on a mat,
Or a frog on a log,
Or a dog,
Or some tea,
Or a flea with a pea,
Or a baked cake,
Or out-of-date sprinkles,
Or even some wrinkles,
Or a rocket with a sprocket,
Or some cherries,
Or some berries,
Or a rooster on a booster!

I know, risk it for a biscuit
With out-of-date sprinkles and some wrinkles!"

Evie Bridges (9)
Grateley Primary School, Grateley

Chocolate Aeroplane

What am I doing here?
It's kind of strange,
I'm on a chocolate aeroplane drinking champagne.
What should I do now?
It's kind of strange,
It's a chocolate aeroplane,
Don't let it melt,
Is it melting? I can't tell,
It's sunny outside
And there is no cloud.
What should I do?
I want to make it to Spain now.

Lara Nassé (11)
Grateley Primary School, Grateley

26

Upside-Down School

It all started off with an upside-down school,
Which had lots of different things, even a pool!
I was really happy to be in this place,
It was really cool, almost like a race!

All the children would mess about and be silly,
Especially this boy in my class named Billy,
Not only us but the teachers as well,
Would have fun and not even bother to ring the bell.

This school was very different,
Different from all the other schools,
I love it, it is my favourite,
It is the upside-down school!

The classrooms are upside down
Oh no! My teacher looks like a clown!
The canteen has turned around,
The hall definitely just made a sound...
Bang! Crash! Whizz! Pop!

Joanna Berhan (10)
Holy Family Catholic Primary School, Park North

Candy Life

I have an invite, wait where is that?
A place full of candy and gummy cats?
"Where could this be?" I started to shout,
The card said, "Well, let's find out!"
In the blink of an eye, I saw something weird,
Not a talking fruit or a silly beard,
But a world full of tasty treats!
Like lollipop trees and sour strip streets.

Children skipping with strawberry laces,
Look at all their smiling faces!
Jiggly jelly pool parties
With yummy, big floating Smarties.
Up in the cotton candy clouds,
People are screaming crazy loud,
Sweet Starburst stars and pomegranate planets,
Gummy rocketships and chocolate cookie comets.

"Let's go to this disco, I'm invited!
This is so cool, I'm so excited!"
First, let's cross the strawberry syrup falls,
Look out! Here come some ice cream balls!

The spicy sriracha volcano is erupting,
It's okay, it's rainbow raining!
Finally, we made it, this is pretty sweet,
Now, let's dance to a delicious disco beat.

Cassandra Jane Cruz (10)

Holy Family Catholic Primary School, Park North

An Evil Cake

Once, there was a cake, cute as can be,
But one day there was a great tragedy,
The cake turned evil, so people called him Evil Cake,
He went in the oven too long so he baked for far too long!
They all tried to make another cake,
But the cake said, "You can't make me go to waste!"

The cake didn't want to be taken,
So he tried to be mistaken,
But, one day the cake turned ginormous,
The town screamed, "It is as scary as a giant snake!"
They cried and said, "How do we save ourselves from a giant cake?"
The cake was monstrous and the people had no idea how to slay the beast.

But, one day, people realised he had to stay,
So they had an idea to just stay and lay,
But, a girl had an idea for the cake,

30

"We can drop it in the lake!"
So they had a plan to make a cake and make the
evil cake go to waste,
The cake found the fake and fell into the lake!
"The cake is over!" they shouted, "Hooray!"

Janina Anne Scot (11)
Holy Family Catholic Primary School, Park North

Football On The Moon

Humankind is in trouble,
The only way is football,
So pack your football boots
And let's go to space!

Once we are in space,
We will need a plan,
So we can beat those no good aliens,
If we lose, we will lose our planet.

Once we score,
There is no need to do more
But to defend,
So let's win this game.

The crowds are cheering,
The game is about to begin,
We score our first goal,
But we don't know that we are floating to the sun!

Nine minutes left until we win our match,
As we fall to our doom
It gets so hot.

Until we notice that we are soon going to die,
Uh-oh! We are floating to the sun,
This is not going to be fun,
But the alien said, "Do not fear!
We have technology that can help you here!"
Don't play football on the moon,
Because you may float to the sun and go boom!

Elvis G (11)

Holy Family Catholic Primary School, Park North

The Fantasy Funfair

It's monster madness at the fantasy funfair,
With knights doing battle or stealing from the dragon's lair,
There are damsels in distress, high up in their towers
And wizards casting spells using magic powers.

The evil elves casting spells, confusing people's minds,
Causing the prince's carriages to start to crash and grind,
The greedy goblins stealing food as soon as they start to feel
That they've decided it's lunchtime and they need a decent meal.

The yeti's yodelling singing notes are making such a blizzard
And the leviathan swimming through the ponds is such a slippery lizard,
The cleaners have a hard job cleaning up the sea serpent's slime,
Or dusting up the knight's armour with disgusting rust and grime.

It's monster madness at the fantasy funfair,
So I suggest a different theme park and advise you
don't go there!

Jacob F

Holy Family Catholic Primary School, Park North

Candy Creation

Candy Creation is a wonderful place,
You won't ever need to find yourself in a race,
The trees are made of candyfloss,
The grass is made of icing frost,
There's a sweet volcano that shoots gummy bears,
Believe me, you'll have the opposite of nightmares.

Caramel, truffles,
Chocolate, waffles,
A lot of gummies and sweet dummies,
Sour and sweet
And candy feet,
Chocolate sundae, this is a fun day!

When night-time falls,
The sugar calls,
The sweets drop down low to the ground,
You'll find yourself in candy heaven,
That's where you'll meet the number seven
Upon the sherbert, upon the cakes,
There is a wonderful chocolate lake.

Cookie bake, cheesecake,
Lemon muffin, candyfloss stuffing,
Banana split, lemon kit,
Chocolate lollies, gummy dollies,
Sour Starburst, ice cream first!

Carly D

Holy Family Catholic Primary School, Park North

One Giant Leap For Cheesekind

Once, there were four friends and not long ago
They took off in their rocket, starting off slow,
They hoped for the best and not the worst,
They got to the moon because they wanted to be
first.

As they landed on the moon, they saw it was made
out of cheese,
They still really liked it as it was better than mushy
green peas,
One small step for man, one giant leap for cheese-
kind
Because this marvellous mission was their biggest
find.

Bang! Pop! That was melted cheese,
So one friend asked, "Can I have some please?"
We then all shouted, "Seize the cheese!"
But then someone asked, "Where are our keys?"

We looked in potholes, craters and pools,
We didn't want anything to let us get fooled,

We took off in our rocket with a big blast
And landed on Earth quickly and fast!

Samuel Antonio Rodrigues (11)
Holy Family Catholic Primary School, Park North

Craziness Above The Cotton Candy Clouds!

Dream of going to Pancake Planet,
Don't worry, imagine turning cookies into cookie comets,
Sour Starburst stars twinkle in the sky,
First, let's eat a perfect pie!

Oops, my tea fell down to the sea, now it's raining rainbow tea,
Just think of indulging in chocolate biscuits,
Now, go and dance to the disco beats,
Chocolate cookies are delicious things,
Come on now, let's eat a gorgeous gummy ring!

Wait, look down, what do you see?
Look! It's a spicy sriracha volcano,
Just look at the spicy lava flow!
Let's make something,
Take a boring biscuit
And take an ice cream and mix it!

Jiggly jelly, wibble wobble,
Let's take a tiny nibble,
Come to the crazy cotton clouds,
Then you will go crazy loud!

Ava D S
Holy Family Catholic Primary School, Park North

A Snow-Filled Desert

Did you know that long ago
Deserts were filled with lots of snow?
There were cold cows,
No one could bow,
It was a dangerous desert!

Sandy snowmen walked around
And they did not fall on the ground!
There were shivering dogs,
Lots of freezing frogs,
It was a dangerous desert!

In the desert today
Nobody can play,
Our desert is hot,
Hotter than a boiling pot,
It is a dangerous desert!

If you look in the sand
You would see this snowy land,
That desert was great,
We came around too late,
It was a dangerous desert!

If you want a barbecue,
That is something you can do
Because in the cold
You grow really old,
It was a dangerous desert!

Dylan Newbury (11)
Holy Family Catholic Primary School, Park North

A Candy Catastrophe

It really is a pity
That it destroyed Jelly Bean City,
Because of the ice cream volcano!

From strawberry to cheese,
"I want raspberry please!"
Old ice cream volcano.

Poor Jelly Bean City,
It really is a pity,
Affected by the flavour wasabi!

Then I saw a lake,
I was sure it was fake
Because it was made of marshmallows!

Marshmallows are sticky,
To some people icky,
So I didn't go anywhere near it!

"This place is weird,"
Said a man with a beard,
So I left as fast as I could!

Boom! Thank goodness it was a dream,
I was definitely going to scream,
I didn't want to get covered with ice cream!

Olivia Connie Lucey (11)
Holy Family Catholic Primary School, Park North

Scrumptious Sweets!

I found a volcano
That had a rainbow
And was filled with scrumptious sweets,
So I climbed in looking for treats!
Oh no! I fell down
And found myself in a whole new town!

I landed on top of candyfloss,
But then I heard a *splish, splash, splosh!*
I realised it came from the chocolate lake
And swimming in it was a delicious cake,
I asked her, "Why are you swimming?"
And she said, "Because I feel like fishing!"

I decided to jump down
And I landed on top of a marshmallow mound,
I saw a lollipop tree
And along came a sweet honeybee,
This is where I wanted to stay,
So I am going to go and play
And find some scrumptious sweets!

Lyllia F (10)
Holy Family Catholic Primary School, Park North

Bean-I-Licious Bath!

A boy named Jake,
Who had a big steak,
Had a large bath full of beans!
His mum walked in and said with a grin,
"What in the world is going on here?"
He said, "Oh dear!
Something horrendous happened here!
But it tastes delicious so I don't care,
Because this bath is very rare!"
His mum heard a *splish, splash splosh!*
And told the boy to have a wash.
Jake said, "No, you have to know, I don't want to
go out and play with Mo!"
He decided to stay inside,
But actually lied,
His mum said, "Come, you have to go outside!"
Jake said, "No, not today, I just want to play in my
bean-i-licious bath!"

Lucy Christina Brown

Holy Family Catholic Primary School, Park North

Eat Some Sweets

In the town, there was a great scare,
Something colourful was coming from the air,
Strange aliens that looked like delicious treats,
But we learned that they weren't very sweet.

They came to invade the town,
They came for the golden crown,
Then it got worse,
They robbed every purse.

The children then realised that, to claim defeat,
They would have to eat,
Later that day there wasn't a treat in sight,
Now the town didn't have to fight.

Now there was a new problem,
The children were causing mayhem,
Children were bouncing off the walls,
They were bouncing like bouncy balls.

How would they solve this problem?

Scarlett Grace Bohane (10)
Holy Family Catholic Primary School, Park North

A Volcanic Wonderland

What do I see? A volcano over there?
Could it be filled with gummy bears?
Are they nice, are they evil?
Let's try them! We should eat them!

Yum, yum, yum! They're delicious,
But they're making me feel malicious,
"Ha ha ha!" Wait, that's not me,
Where am I? Where could I be?

What is this? A candy land?
Is that road made of sweets or sand?
Look over there, a talking book!
Come with me, let's take a look.

There's a recipe, I wonder what it's for,
There are candy canes, gummy bears and more!
Whoa! This is some book,
Maybe I should take more than just a look...

Lisa K (11)
Holy Family Catholic Primary School, Park North

Gummy Bears Invade Earth

Welcome to Loopy Land,
In here, we all lend a helping hand,
So if you're in a muddle,
You won't fall in a puddle.

But, one day
In May,
An experiment was taking place,
For a super secret case.

But, instead,
While gummy bears were still in bed,
They spilt the potion,
Gummies are getting into motion.

As the gummy bears grew and grew,
The villagers all knew,
They all knew they were going to be eaten,
But before that, they were going to be beaten.

Bears were flying from the air,
Soon, they were going to die,
Gummy bears invading the land,
Now we can't lend a helping hand.

Lena Tomaszewicz (11)

Holy Family Catholic Primary School, Park North

The Oddest Day Of The Year

One day a year
Is the one that no one likes to hear,
When positives become negatives,
When classical become groovy rivs,
I had to put underwear on my head,
I had to sleep under my bed,
Cuts felt nice, bruises were Heaven
And the weather outside felt like minus eleven!

All happy people had to show their bad side
And don't get me started on what it's like outside!
Planes got around on the ground,
I heard a quiet, "Meow," from a greyhound,
The moon shone brightly at 9am,
Now the sun is shining at 8pm.
I'm trying to sleep in the sun's rays,
Praying that there will be better days.

Nathan Sibunga (10)
Holy Family Catholic Primary School, Park North

Cookie Destruction

Once, there was a cute cookie in Candy Land,
But one day, the cookie turned evil and became huge!
The candy people called him Cookie Monster,
The cookie went into the oven too long and he burnt,
For the first week, people attacked and he got hurt,
So he tried to flirt,
But it didn't work.

So cookie decided to take over the world,
So then he could have a twirl
And get a chocolate pearl,
So he will not be concerned.

So he took over the world full of candy,
But, once he was done, he felt rather sandy,
The cookie tried to make them come back to life
But it didn't work.

Aydann O
Holy Family Catholic Primary School, Park North

What Type Of Planet Am I On Now?

Burping ants,
Farting cows,
What kind of planet am I on now?
I can't believe there are hairy seals
And spying cockerels in the fields,
Sharks have legs and snakes have arms,
Big buff pigs run all the farms,
There's a food kebab with slimy fries,
Oh, and did I mention there's a mud pie?

I went down deep into the sea,
Found dogs with gills,
Hamsters with tails,
Cats have these frills,
Whales have no mouth,
Crabs have ten tails,
Seashells have twenty nails,
But, now I'm on a planet filled with tails,
So can I ask
What planet am I on now?

Elga (11)
Holy Family Catholic Primary School, Park North

Food Vs Sweets

On the plate,
The little piece of bacon had a mate,
His mate was the overweight pizza,
That was taken out by a gummy laser,
The first man on Mars was
The sweet wrapper,
The gummy bears shot their
Strawberry flares,
When the enormous fork
Sliced the helpless pork,
A strip of candyfloss,
Called Mr Pink Brain,
Suddenly shed lots of pain,
So the food fought back,
But there were more sweets in the rack,
So the food was outnumbered
And that's a fact,
On the battlefield, there were only broken shields,
On the gummy fields...

Alfie Guy (11)
Holy Family Catholic Primary School, Park North

The Dancing Queen

There was a dancing llama,
Dancing like an embarrassing Mama,
Dancing like a headless chicken,
Having groovy moves and kickin',
Twirling around and around,
Yet the llama was dancing without a sound!
Shaking its furry butt,
While the starry sky was shut,
Then, a huge, shining disco ball
Spun around and started to fall.

The majestic llama danced all types,
But ballet always gave her a fright,
She was the absolute best at pop!
Whenever I dance to it, I flop.
All the animals have seen
That the llama is the marvellous dancing queen!

Nutchtayla (11)
Holy Family Catholic Primary School, Park North

Swimming On Jupiter!

As I'm swimming on Jupiter,
I find that I'm getting stupider,
I'm starting to feel really cool
As I'm swimming in the pool.

The water is made of Fanta,
So all my friends start to banter,
I start to get a sugar rush,
But my friends tell me to hush!

I decided to dive in,
But I landed in the bin!
Suddenly, a dragon chases me,
So I flew like a flea.

I think I deserve a treat
Because I've been super sweet!
Maybe a chocolate bar
Whilst I'm playing on my gummy guitar.

Olivia O'Malley
Holy Family Catholic Primary School, Park North

Fantastic Fanta Party On Mars

On Mars, we drink Fanta,
We drink it, we sip it, we banter,
The aliens dancing, jumping around,
On this huge party, there's lots of sound.

There are drinks, food and aliens,
We had lots of fun whilst eating lime,
But, you know old Bill, he turned into slime!

Volcanos full of flowing Fanta lava,
But some came and shouted, "Get out!"
This soon made a big palaver.

So, then the Fanta party had to shut,
So I called my friends at Pizza Hut!

Kaitlyn S
Holy Family Catholic Primary School, Park North

The Beast

The Minotaur is a fearsome beast,
A creature you would want to see the least,
With glistening red eyes
That reflect across the skies,
Every year sent a gruesome feast.

The king's knights sent people for the vicious beast,
Who loved his bloody feast,
If you would have been in his path,
That would not have been a happy laugh.

I warn you not to come to this island,
Make sure you avoid this violence,
This creature should be thrown away,
I warn you, stay away!

Callum P
Holy Family Catholic Primary School, Park North

Candy Battle

Once, in Candy Land,
There was an attack!
Gummy bears came from above,
I wanted to run back,
But could I fly?

I flew up and then I gasped,
"A gummy bear maker! What luck!"
But how could I stop them?
What could I do?

I flew closer
And then I saw,
Long, red, strawberry cables
Hanging from the door.

I started cutting,
It didn't work,
But, just that moment
It went...

David P
Holy Family Catholic Primary School, Park North

My Little Fairy

There's a storm and it's very scary,
The one thing that could help me is my little fairy,
I saw a chair and decided to hide under it
Because there's thunder!

And horrible flashes of lightning,
It's really frightening,
She covered me in fairy dust
And told me she will save us!

Me and my fairy have a special bond,
As she waves her magic wand,
She was gone!
I wonder when I will see her again?

Lucy Charlotte King (10)
Holy Family Catholic Primary School, Park North

The Overweight Cow

While eating mouth-watering popcorn,
An overweight cow lay in the emerald meadow,
Chewing a full bag of it.
Gulp! It went down,
In the cow's stomach,
All of a sudden, this happened...
Blegh! The poor cow was sick!
Everywhere in the meadow,
The unwell cow mooed for help,
Feeling very awful and cheerless
And he thought to himself,
Maybe I shouldn't have eaten so much popcorn!

Lacey Blayney (11)
Holy Family Catholic Primary School, Park North

The Weird Flying Man

I saw the weirdest thing today,
It was so weird and daft, absolutely nuts!
A man came by, but he wasn't walking,
He was flying like a bird!
Literally,
He was waving his arms and legs about,
Like bird's wings flapping about,
He was yelling,
"Bgar bgar bgar!"
It was such a random moment in my life,
So now, I think I'm scarred for life!
No really... I actually am!

Toby Trueman (11)
Holy Family Catholic Primary School, Park North

Time Travel

Time flew by... *whoosh!*
We could see the sky,
The clock was thinking,
We were all blinking,
The clock struck ten,
We could see Ben,
He joined in the fun,
We were all laughing and chewing gum,
Glancing at the clock,
We hid just around the block,
Then we saw inside the clock, a dot,
We had to all say goodbye,
Ben then disappeared
In the blink of an eye!

Chloe Anne Bird (11)

Holy Family Catholic Primary School, Park North

A Fast Food And Dessert Land

My fast food and dessert land started off in a
craze,
A chicken nugget found a land
Made of fast foods and dessert,
Nugget found fries as friends
As doughnuts fell off the end.

Doughnut met a chocolate bar
And melted onto it
As they set off on an insane adventure
(They made sure to take a spare denture!)
An adventure to a never-explored land!

Zosia Bachniak (11)
Holy Family Catholic Primary School, Park North

Upside-Down World

Could you imagine
In an upside-down world...
A flying bird
As quick as in a race,
That hits your smooth face
Like it doesn't even care,
Like honey on a bear,
It cannot be true!
There's a monkey on the loo,
From the magical broom,
That can't be uncursed,
Oh no!
Oh, help!
The house is gonna burst!

Amelia Dulik (11)
Holy Family Catholic Primary School, Park North

The Devil In A Teddy Toy

Mum and Dad bought a teddy toy,
Every night it turns off my light
And my bear comes to life...
It will make my pug talk and act like a person!

So, every night I sprint downstairs,
Peek and my parents are fast asleep,
Then spring back upstairs
And see my teddy everywhere!
I feel like I'm in some sort of curse!

Andrew Wallis (11)

Holy Family Catholic Primary School, Park North

Man-Eating Chicken

One day, I went to town,
A chicken then ate a clown,
So I ran as fast as I could,
Then the chicken ate some wood,
I looked up to the sky,
Then I saw something fly,
I wiped my face with a towel,
Then I saw a flying cow,
I went home and heard ticking,
Then I saw the giant chicken...

Grace O'Malley (11)

Holy Family Catholic Primary School, Park North

Super Cat

A super cat can message his friends and family,
A super cat can play games, eat cake and sweets
and even have a birthday party,
A super cat can talk to other cats about discos,
A super cat can dance with alien robots,
A super cat can fly to South America to meet his
friends.

Angel Qumar (11)
Holy Family Catholic Primary School, Park North

Megan's Easter Eggs

M is for Megan

E is for Easter

G is for gobbling all my eggs up

A is for another egg found

N is for no more chocolate eggs left for Megan to gobble up.

Megan Costello (10)

Holy Family Catholic Primary School, Park North

Riding Free

Summer winds fan the grass and whip the horse's mane,
They travel, horse and rider, through a sea of twinkling rain,
There is no trail, they follow no path that can be seen,
They travel, horse and rider, creating quite a scene,
The beauty of the horse's stride, the pattern of his hooves,
Takes the ride to a place that within the world removes,
Ahead is just open land, like the future path
And mountains symbolise your highest daily climb,
As clouds roll by and hills elope,
You grip tight to his sides and hurry on for an awesome ride,
That means to you, perhaps, freedom of independence,
A day you can create,
A day to stand upright with a proud and certain gait.

Hope Blossom Morgan-Hilliar (9)
Medina Primary School, Cosham

The Cat's Restaurant

The Cat's Restaurant is a great place to be,
From an enormous, huge elephant to a tiny, small flea.

The fluffy cat chef is a brilliant cook,
He can make cat food pizza and worm spaghetti, without using a recipe book.

All the animals are so excited, the Cat's Restaurant is the place to go,
There's a flying squirrel and a chocolate eating snake putting on a show.

The animals' chatter, amazingly in English,
The food is so delicious, it isn't hard to demolish.

Why don't you come to the fabulous Cat's Restaurant?
You can eat and stay for as long as you want!

Oliver Stagg (8)
Medina Primary School, Cosham

Hear A Baby Ladybird Sing

Monkey, Cockroach and the tree
Were all very happy,
Waiting to buy tickets
That they caught at the last minute,
Little Ladybird was sitting there,
Glad to be singing upstairs,
Baby Ladybird started,
Tree and Monkey were excited,
Cockroach was licking a lolly,
He was cheeky and naughty,
The song was finished happily,
Cockroach and Monkey clapped loudly
And Tree waved branches kindly,
Tree went back to the jungle,
Monkey and Cockroach cuddled,
Little Ladybird was tired,
She bumbled away,
It was a really nice weekend.

Farin Salehabadi (8)
Medina Primary School, Cosham

The Birthday Monster

B irthdays come once a year,

D on't try to see, do not stare,
A ll your dreams he makes come true,
Y our birthday wish he brings to you,

M onsters are smart,
O ne peek and you're asleep,
N obody will remember,
S unrises to keep,
T o come to your house, he uses a magic door,
E ntering in, leaving presents on the floor,
R emember not to complain. Or he won't come again!

Edward Patrick Simmons (9)

Medina Primary School, Cosham

Shark In A Bath

I looked through the door hole,
I couldn't see anything except for a mole,
Until I looked closely and saw a shark,
So I tried to kick the door, but it just made a mark,
It was sleeping in the bath
And I just wanted to laugh,
I could hear it snoring,
But it was really annoying,
So I had had enough
And I decided to be rough,
I kicked the door open wide,
But it was just a dog in a shark suit on the side!

Jacey Bamba (9)
Medina Primary School, Cosham

Have A Genie As A Pet

Have a genie as a pet,
Three wishes they will grant,
Have a genie as a pet
And the world you could just get.
Have a genie as a pet,
Think of what you could possibly get,
From animals to phones, you could get one of both
of those,
Have a genie as your pet,
I don't think you'll ever forget,
Have a genie as a pet,
The pet you won't forget.

Lola Wilbur (9)
Medina Primary School, Cosham

My Day At School

Last time I went to school
I had a terrible day,
I pleaded with my mother,
But she just turned away!

So I went to school
And everyone laughed at me,
So I turned away
And said, "Good day," to the twins.

At lunch we had soggy stew,
I hate it, don't you know
And when I refused to eat it,
She threw me in the snow!

Gracie Walters (9)
Medina Primary School, Cosham

My Hair Almost Strangled Me

I had just woken up,
Things were not as they seemed,
My neck was quite squashed,
It was like I had dreamed!

My hair was flying everywhere,
It just wouldn't sit down,
I didn't know what to do,
I could only frown.

Then, it attacked me!
Oh, what had I done?
It piled on my head,
I didn't know it weighed a tonne!

It then changed its mind,
This was far too much,
How could I stop it?
Maybe with my brush?

I looked everywhere for it,
It couldn't have disappeared!
If I couldn't find it,
It was just as I had feared!

Where had I left it?
Was it under the sink?
I had to hurry up,
My neck was starting to shrink!

Finally, I found it,
Hidden under my play,
I gripped my hairbrush,
I had to do this straight away!

I made it sit down,
I could dance with glee,
It was so close,
My hair almost strangled me!
(Luckily, it didn't.)

Maanya Sekhar (11)
Red Oaks Primary School, Swindon

A Fish Stuck In A Tree

Is that really what I think I see?
Is that really a fish stuck in a tree?
How does it move around and breathe
And walk around so gracefully?
Shouldn't it be in a pond or the sea
Where it can survive healthily?

How has it been up there so long?
Oh and now it's bursting into song!
And now, with a friend, it's playing ping-pong!
Can someone please tell me how it's so strong?
Please correct me if I'm wrong,
But this fish is not where it belongs!

And now it's starting a speech to prove,
That even fish can groove,
Walk, talk and even move,
Many people have politely disapproved,
However, many people also approve,
But in the end, no one could see
How a fish became stuck in a tree!

Emily Norris (11)
Red Oaks Primary School, Swindon

When Mars Stuck With Earth

In my bed, I was one morning,
Nothing to do, it was boring,
When I heard something from afar,
Maybe it was just a big, big car?
Then, I saw a flash of light,
To me, it was quite bright,
Was it the sun or a star?
I didn't know, I was eating a chocolate bar,
After a while, I could finally see,
Then I realised that I needed to wee,
When I came back, I saw something strange,
Did our solar system have something changed?
The planet missing was what we call Mars,
The same name as my chocolate bar!
I could see it on the other side of the Earth,
Something that looked like a newborn birth,
One half of Mars was stuck with one half of Earth,
Now I know what this world is worth!

Sami Khan (11)
Red Oaks Primary School, Swindon

Family

I am Kevin,
I look over the land.
I am a father.

I have a wife,
With her head in the clouds,
She is a mother.

We have two children called Ash and Flo,
Who are always fighting with each other.
This makes the village panic and fluster,
Does this make us a bad mother and father?

We live in a village, covered in molten lava,
Because our children are always angry with each other.
I look down on a lake, it has shiny crystal water,
This is the only land that is not covered in our children's molten lava.

Eliza Bates (11)
St Barnabas Primary School, Market Lavington

Explosion

E verlasting ash cloud parading across the land,

X -raying lava rushing down, making crashes,

P ushing hot magma up the steaming vent,

L osing control and spitting out lava,

O ver-the-top boom rumbling,

S pitting out magma and throwing out ash,

I nside, bubbling lava flows like a river stream,

O vercast winds blowing the ash further than the eye can see,

N ew core helps to shake the magma up to the top.

Jamie Saunders (10)

St Barnabas Primary School, Market Lavington

Explosive

E ruptions were worrying, deadly,

e **X** iting rapidly from the medium-sized hole,

P oisonous, scorching, red-hot lava,

L ava pool,

O ozing rapidly out the cone-shaped volcano,

S pitting, bubbling, streaming lava pouring out,

I ntensely bursting, scorching liquids,

V olcanic pressures,

E xpelling, gurgling, burping bubbles.

Maisie Ann Rodger (11)

St Barnabas Primary School, Market Lavington

Vicious

V anished with a click,

O ozing magma melting into lava,

L ots of scared, screaming people,

"C alm! Please be calm!" people are saying,

A lthough people are scared, there is a strange beauty to the volcano,

"N o!" people are screaming as their homes are vanishing by the second,

"O h..." they are saying once their homes have disappeared.

Ruby McLellan (10)

St Barnabas Primary School, Market Lavington

Lava

L ooping, swirling, shooting lava going to the sky and the ground,

A ll I see are ashes flowing with the wind, lava oozing all over the place,

V olcano, do you want friends? Because it seems like you're a monster, a killer, you're taking innocent people,

A pparently you're a monster, are you happy, sad? Something else? Why is your magma coming out of you?

Mollie Rodger (9)

St Barnabas Primary School, Market Lavington

Running Fire

Dribbling across the ground,
Swallowing what it has found,
It dries, then cracks,
Then never comes back.
Ash clouds form,
Covering the ground
From what it has found.
In the path of lava
You shall die,
Even if you hide high.
Lava running free,
Coming and surrounding me.
Then, it is dormant.

Isabel Josse Chammings (9)
St Barnabas Primary School, Market Lavington

Volcanoes

Volcanoes' magma oozing,
Like fireworks, it's booming.

The ground rattles
As the lava crackles.

Killing amounts of ash,
Don't forget the death-defying sounds.

Trees and ground get battered,
The ground is full of clatter.

The lava bubbles,
Like he's in trouble.

Matilda Sharp (10)
St Barnabas Primary School, Market Lavington

Big Red

V ery powerful it will be,

O ozing out boiling liquid,

L ots of noise it will make,

C omes for your life and kills,

A sh flying through the air,

N ightmares for most people,

O ddly exploding out of nowhere.

Cameron Maxwell (11)

St Barnabas Primary School, Market Lavington

Boiled

As the raging beast comes alive
Lava enters the earth,
The bubbling magma comes oozing out,
The volcano is at birth.

Thundering ash clouds get bigger,
Destructive rocks come spitting,
Explosions in the air like fireworks,
Rocks sink into the ground like they're sitting.

Toby Morgan (10)
St Barnabas Primary School, Market Lavington

Magma

M olten lava licks the earth, like a frog when it catches a fly,

A round the world, they erupt one by one,

G o, go, go, run fast, fast, fast!

M y, oh my, don't go slow when you feel low,

A re you ever going to go?

Jake Dyer (11)

St Barnabas Primary School, Market Lavington

The Land Of The Volcanoes

My volcano land has...
Magma oozing out of it,
Amazing colours.
Vicious and angry,
Oozing lava.
Lava as hot as the sun,
Colossal in size.
Always erupting,
Nobody is safe!
Oozing, oozing, oozing.

Isla Mughal (10)
St Barnabas Primary School, Market Lavington

Giant Peak

G urgling lava gushing down,
I ncreasing the amount of hot, rocky magma,
A sh cloud exploding loudly,
N othing left within its path,
T errifying, rumbling earth.

Charlie Ottaway (9)

St Barnabas Primary School, Market Lavington

Run

Lava pours and dribbles,
It makes massive or small ripples
Before it shoots out
From its extremely hot spout!
Ash covers the land,
Louder than a pop band,
Ruby-red lava pours to his feet,
Run away Pete!

Katie Swanborough (11)
St Barnabas Primary School, Market Lavington

Red Hot

V olcanic activity,

O ozing magma,

L oud bangs,

C olliding lava,

A bandoning villages,

N ervous screams,

O bliterating.

Harley James Williams (10)

St Barnabas Primary School, Market Lavington

Monster

I am angry,
I am mad,
I am doing something bad,
I would go and catch a plane,
I'm erupting every day,
So I would stay away.

Katie Stabbins (11)
St Barnabas Primary School, Market Lavington

Hot Lava

L ava is boiling,

A mazing,

V olcanoes are erupting,

A sh clouds bursting through the sky.

Millie Winstanley (9)
St Barnabas Primary School, Market Lavington

Great Wonderland

It is hot,
It is not,
When it is done
It will not run,
But when it still flows
You must go!

Ben Smith (10)
St Barnabas Primary School, Market Lavington

Flying On A Doughnut

I'm flying on a doughnut,
I'm right up in the sky,
All the breeze is blowing in my face,
I'm spinning like mad.

Who would know that a doughnut could fly,
Turn and spin and all of that,
Go up and down and all around
High up in the sky?

The chocolate is melting,
The sprinkles are in my eyes,
It's nearly time for bed,
The sky is dark,
I just saw an island far away.

There's a super glazed sun,
Marshmallow birds and candyfloss clouds,
I rubbed my eyes, it was unbelievable!
That's the time that I flew on a doughnut!

Elsie Lowrie (8)
St Catherine's Catholic Primary School, Stratton

Dragons Vs Gorillas

I saw ninjas
Training gorillas
To defeat the dragons.
I could hear the dragons,
With hats made of potato,
Coming our way.
I could feel the ground
Crack under my feet
And, finally, the gorillas were ready.

It was an intense battle,
But the dragons won.
The dragons won
Because they could make fireballs
And they could breathe fire.
Just at the last moment,
I saw a potion
And drank it
And when a dragon shot a fireball
I disappeared.

After that, I started to be silly,
I jumped into a pool full of sharks,
I jumped into a volcano,
I threw up in a pool of acid,
I even ate a rainbow
And I did even more crazy things!

Atkins Tofilo Msury (9)
St Catherine's Catholic Primary School, Stratton

Marshmallows Coming To Life

It was a lovely summer's day in Candy Land
And you could hear fun music all around
And all you could see was candy everywhere.

There were marshmallows and they were microscopic,
Gummy bears crashed into both of the marshmallows,
Some sort of magic happened.

The marshmallows came to life!
They started jumping around and eating all of the candy,
They were up to mischief and ate the gummy bear's house!
They got super fluffy,
They were walking and the gummy bear crashed into the marshmallows again,
So they shrank and they weren't alive anymore.

Elyanna Jackson (8)
St Catherine's Catholic Primary School, Stratton

Crisp Frames

I was playing with
Egyptians and games
And we went inside
And we saw new window frames.

They weren't made of wood,
No, not anymore,
They were made of crisps!
Well, that's not what they're for!

As long as my dad made it,
People came to see,
Just when my mum made a sign
For my sister and me!

But people started eating,
My mum and dad did shout,
"Please don't eat our crispy frame,
It's just our lovely house!"

Oliver Truchanowicz (9)
St Catherine's Catholic Primary School, Stratton

The Candy Land

There was a candy cane lamp post,
I licked and licked until...
My tongue got stuck!

Skydiving through candyfloss clouds,
While I did it
I tried to eat it,
But I got a beard of it instead!

Oh, it's snowing!
Whipped cream,
Yum, yum, yum in my tum,
Normally, hail would be annoying,
But not this hail,
This is sugar!

Ooh, swimming in syrup,
I like the sound of that,
Half an hour later
A little help?
I'm stuck!

Conall McFarnon (8)
St Catherine's Catholic Primary School, Stratton

The Strangle Plants

One day, I was falling from the sky
Forever, I never stopped falling
I fell in a magical forest,
I fell on a bouncy mushroom
I squished a really weird animal,
I saw biscuit skateboard, people in bubbles
And houses made out of jelly
An ogre told me that something dangerous
happens at night.
I started walking and walking and I was in a forest
I saw plants coming alive
They wanted to strangle you,
You just had to get past them and then,
There was a chest...

Juan Andres Guanchez (8)
St Catherine's Catholic Primary School, Stratton

A Tea Party With An Elephant

There's an elephant in my house,
He's drinking all my tea,
I don't know what to do,
He's just chilling with me.

He's eating all my lollipops,
He's munching all my sweets.
I don't know what to say except,
"Will you have a tea party with me?"

So, we bring out all the tea
And pass around the cups
And then we get the cakes, which are all eaten up,
"Oh, I'm glad you're here with me!"

Maimie Belcher (8)
St Catherine's Catholic Primary School, Stratton

The Land Of Craziness

The trees are pink candyfloss,
It rains mint ice cream,
And the people are gummy bears.
A candy cane is a helter-skelter,
The snow is sugar,
The birds are paper birds.
The planets are different kinds of food.
Sausage dogs are sausages,
Houses are made out of crisps,
And balloons are bubbles.
Penguins can fly high in the sky,
Handles are strawberry jelly,
Water is syrup,
And dictionaries can talk
In my imagination!

Eleanor Davis (8)
St Catherine's Catholic Primary School, Stratton

The Dancing Nail!

I am in the kitchen, doing my nails,
I take a look and my nail falls off!
I look on the floor,
I see it dance!
It has apparently turned magic,
Is this a dream or is this real?
I jump on the cooker,
I run for my life,
I try not to die,
My heart skips a beat,
The nails are huge and pink,
When I wake up, I find out it was fake,
So I walk into the kitchen,
"Ahh!"
The dancing nail!
It is real!

Victoria Skoczek (8)
St Catherine's Catholic Primary School, Stratton

The Cow Lady

In the world of space,
But not any old space,
Was a cow girl,
I saw her,
I did, I did, I did,
I'm serious!
But the planets here were bushes,
Big, hairy bushes,
There were aliens and mermaids.

The cow girl was riding
On a star, a big, shiny star,
There were mermaids,
They had wonderful scales,
I saw green aliens,
But they hid in bushes,
It was more than amazing!

Elsie Anello (9)
St Catherine's Catholic Primary School, Stratton

On A Doughnut

In the big, fluffy sky I flew
On a doughnut,
I went up high in the sky.

I saw a beach down below,
It was shiny and amazing,
I went across the shallow water.

I saw Ireland up ahead,
I got there and it was amazing,
Then I flew down.

I woke up on the beach tent,
It was a magical night,
Also, my mum gave me a doughnut,
Everyone had a doughnut by morning light.

Jack Parker (8)
St Catherine's Catholic Primary School, Stratton

Sunbathing On The Sun

I was sunbathing on the sun
With no sun cream,
No hats and no shade,
The heat was preposterous!
Ouch!

I was there for three weeks,
I was a melted man,
The scorching sun was frying me up,
Ouch!

I invented something brand new,
Sunbathing on the scorching sun!
Ouch!

Back down I came from the sun,
With a grin on my face,
Gosh, that was a good time!
Ouch!

Joseph Szymon Mobey (8)
St Catherine's Catholic Primary School, Stratton

Syrup-Man

When I was a kid
I always wanted a pool full of syrup,
But, suddenly, *bam!*
The syrup pool was just laying
In my exquisite backyard!
I took a run up
And a big jump.
I got stuck and I tried screaming for help,
Suddenly, a hand came out of nowhere,
It grabbed me,
It was my dad,
We couldn't get the syrup off
So my dad started to call me Syrup-Man!

Archie Leddy (9)
St Catherine's Catholic Primary School, Stratton

Candyland Decides!

The candy adventure didn't go as planned...

Because there were lanky birds all around,
Everyone around had Twizzler hair
Except for me,
I was just in despair!
I had to go down
A gummy bear slide,
With magic dragons all around,
I felt all the trees melting,
I had to run,
While I was waiting,
Everything was dark and melting
Then I fell asleep.

Maja Skowron (9)
St Catherine's Catholic Primary School, Stratton

Magic Carpet Which Travelled Through Space

The magic carpet drove me to space,
It was crazy and fast,
We landed on enormous planets which we visited,
The alien chased us but we escaped,
We saw a billion stars,
When we got closer to the stars, there were
looming lava balls,
They were enormous,
We saw a planet that looked like a cheeseburger,
It looked crazy!
After that, the magic carpet drove me home to
Earth.

Jan Graz (8)
St Catherine's Catholic Primary School, Stratton

The Clouds Are Pink Candyfloss

In the world of candy
Was a lonely candyfloss cloud,
When people saw it, they felt vacant,
It was rosy and flawless.

The cloud sat impeccably,
Alone, yet standing out,
It was pink and fluffy,
You could see it from miles away.

Bloodshot eyes looked at the cloud,
It was the most beautiful thing,
People had no words when they saw it!

Ciaran Hamilton (9)
St Catherine's Catholic Primary School, Stratton

Popcorn Pops In A Fridge

This popcorn pops in the fridge,
No one really knows why,
This popcorn is special,
Surely, everyone knows that?
This popcorn pops in the fridge,
It is my story, why?

Is this real?
Or just a dream?
Oh my, it is real!
I went downstairs,
Opened the fridge
And the popcorn was popping,
Pop! Pop! Pop!

Amelia Kunz (9)

St Catherine's Catholic Primary School, Stratton

Flying Furniture

My shelf just levitated,
Right off the floor
And tipped all of my pictures,
Which all smashed on the floor.

My table hit my light bulb,
Which shattered on the floor,
Then, the table smashed me,
Bang! Right in the face.

I had to leave my house,
I walked right to my friends
And then bought a new house.

Gavin Chen (9)
St Catherine's Catholic Primary School, Stratton

Weird Day

It was a cold day on the beach,
It was Wednesday and everything went weird,
A bird was lying on me,
A fish was dancing on the water
And there was a slug in the air,
The bird pooed on me,
The fish backflipped and hit its head
And fell into the water
And the slug dropped,
Suddenly, they all went away...

Zac Smith (9)
St Catherine's Catholic Primary School, Stratton

Buzz!

I walk through a mushroom,
As small as I can be,
But never eat a biscuit
That says, "I'm a bee!"

I have yellow stripes
All over my back,
I even have some black.

I have some floppy things as well,
I think they're white,
They are very weird,
I want to bite!

Florence Zajt (9)
St Catherine's Catholic Primary School, Stratton

Talking Clocks

Back at school,
Clocks are ticking,
We hear a noise,
The clocks are talking.

Clocks are saying,
"8! 8:01! 8:02!"
Everyone's irritated,
Everyone's mad!

Clocks are flying around,
Acting crazy,
What should we do?
Time is not ticking but it's talking!

Leah Antionette Quinn (9)
St Catherine's Catholic Primary School, Stratton

Woke Up Funny

I woke up funny
On my belly,
Birds tweeting in my ear,
Last of the oxygen
In my lungs,
I was floating,
I was in the sky,
I whispered to a bird,
"Teach me how to fly?"
He whispered to me
And took me to a land
To teach me how to fly,
Fly away for ever and ever and ever.

Sienna Meade (8)
St Catherine's Catholic Primary School, Stratton

Tea With A Tiger

I invited a tiger to tea,
He started to eat all of my cookies,
He put them into my tea,
I wish I never invited him,
But now he's chilling with me.

I invited a tiger to tea,
A colossal tiger in a wonky room
On a tiny chair,
Drinking tea with me.

Wiktoria Wozniak (9)
St Catherine's Catholic Primary School, Stratton

Hypnotising Fish

I was underwater
With no one else,
But then I saw a fish,
But there was something weird about this fish,
It was holding something in its fin,
It was a coin on a piece of string,
The next thing I know, I was asleep.

Austin Geoff Jones (9)
St Catherine's Catholic Primary School, Stratton

Candy Land

I ran through a portal,
Bang!
I was in a world of candy,
Then I saw an ice cream house,
I could not believe it,
There were real gummy bears,
I was like, someone pinched me!
It was so astonishing!

Harley Gwazeni (9)
St Catherine's Catholic Primary School, Stratton

I Don't Want To Go To School Mum

"Mum! I'm sick!
Mum! I've broken my leg!
Mum! I have chickenpox!
Mum! School is cancelled!"
"Okay dear," said Mum.

"How was your day dear?" said Mum,
"It was good thanks,"
"That's good, and how are your teachers?" said
Mum,
"Super funny, they're great!"
"That's great! You must be glad that school wasn't
cancelled
And your leg isn't broken,
And you're not sick
And you don't have chickenpox!" said Mum,
"Yes Mum, I love school!"

Sandy Evans (10)
St John's CE Primary School, Tisbury

The Animals In My Head

Every night I go to bed
With wild animals in my head,
Reindeer prancing on my bed
And proud parakeets prancing with my ted.

On my floor, the lions' roar,
The cheetahs cheat at cards,
The wolves keep score upon their paws
And the alert giraffes stand guard.

In my wardrobe, the monkeys swing,
They love to play and dance all day,
The meerkats stand up tall and proud
And then begin to sing.

As I slowly drift off to sleep,
With all the noises around,
Above my head, I count the sheep,
Until there is no sound.

Maisie Burt (11)
St John's CE Primary School, Tisbury

The Letter

Dear Mr Brown,

I'm so sorry to see you down,
I've baked you a pie,
I think it will match your tie,
Don't frown,
This will cheer up the whole town.

I hope you like the pie,
Goodbye,

From the little girl down the road!

Grace Major (10)
St John's CE Primary School, Tisbury

Stuck In My Bubble!

I got stuck in my bubblegum,
My sticky bubble I got stuck in,
I drifted off to the stars above,
I drifted, I drifted, I drifted off far,
I saw a flash, I heard a bang,
A snappy dragon came to pop my bubble!
He used his claws to scratch and scratch,
But the bubble did not pop and never stopped,
I flew to the moon made of icing,
The dragon evolved into a glowing phoenix
As bright as the shimmering sun,
He swooped and popped my bubblegum bubble
With his fiery feather of fire,
The phoenix took me home as fast as the wind,
Forever my friend he will be,
I was stuck in bubblegum,
A bubble I was stuck in,
Never, ever again will I blow bubblegum!

Mya Sales (9)
St Mark's CE Junior School, Salisbury

Cosmic Confusion

I look up at the sky
And what do I see?
Jupiter, Saturn, all the planets floating free,
But something doesn't look right with them all,
I look again and I see a beach ball!
But then, I realise it's not just that planet,
The sky has changed, how dramatic!
The sun's a potato with cheesy hot sauce,
The moon is a hay bale being nibbled by a horse!
Saturn's a burger with an onion ring round,
Then I see a Malteser falling down to the ground.
I walk up the beach to have a bath in the ocean,
But then I realise, I forgot my lotion!
Then I feel a pinch
And I wake up to see,
My mum and dad standing right before me!

Carla Carpenter-Paya (9)
St Mark's CE Junior School, Salisbury

I Met A Fairy!

I met a fairy,
Her name was Mary,
She really wasn't scary.
She was doing her magic
Up in the attic,
She was creating a rainbow
Over her halo.
Then I fell over
So she came over,
She gave me a toy
Which brought me great joy,
I told her that I really want to fly,
But even though she was shy,
She let me have fun
Whilst flying in the sun,
When we were on our way back,
She fell on the ground with a splat!
Her pixie dust had run out,
But she walked like a Scout!
When I got back,
There she was sat,

But then she took flight,
It gave me such a fright,
I met a fairy,
Her name was Mary,
She really wasn't scary!

Annabel Robyn Leonie Arnold (9)

St Mark's CE Junior School, Salisbury

Riding A Lightning Bolt

Quick as a flash,
I flew through the sky,
At the start line, I joyfully waved goodbye,
Still miles to go,
Though I had an ecstatic glow,
I'd race any of the following,
Rain, hail or snow!

The finish line stood ahead,
When I felt a burst of pride blow to my head,
It was definitely better than sleeping late in bed,
Now, I know what you're thinking...

Whatever did I ride?
Top tip, never ride it inside,
Okay, as long as it's between you and me,
Come close and listen carefully,
Drum roll, please... A lightning bolt!
Of course, that's how I rode it with such ease.

Izzie Davies-Evans (9)
St Mark's CE Junior School, Salisbury

My Trip To Wonderland!

I woke up one ordinary day
And decided to go to Wonderland Bay!
I...

Had an underwater BBQ (it didn't go very well!)
Jumped on a cactus (I don't want to talk about it),
Drove a submarine around the shops,
Fried cheesy moon rocks (yummy!)
Played hopscotch with a giant (it was not easy!)
Made a house out of crisps.
Sunbathed on a cloud (ahh!)
Learnt to speak Alien,
Licked a shark (don't ask!)

It was the end of the day
At Wonderland Bay,
I lay down in my bed,
In my house of crisps
And blew bubbles into moon craters.

Nyah Rose Gordon (10)
St Mark's CE Junior School, Salisbury

Dream Adventure

When Mum and Dad are asleep at night,
Me and my dog Winnie,
We pack a torch and we pack a snack
And put them in a big rucksack.

We go to a world where elephants fly,
Where unicorns are real
And monkeys eat banana pie.
Winnie swims in a river of gold
And I look into a mirror that turns me old.

When the birds start singing,
It's time to go home,
Sneak back into our beds,
Hopefully Mum and Dad won't know!

Kaci-May Dempsey (7)
St Mark's CE Junior School, Salisbury

The Moon

When I go out at night
And see the ice-cold moon,
It glimmers in the evening light
And sparkles in the gloom.

Its brilliant light shines on the spot
Where I stand, gazing around,
I wonder at the amazing gleam
That is scattered all over the ground.

Then, suddenly, the light grows brighter
As the night falls slowly down,
The moon floats away with the stars
That I shall see again after sundown.

Holly Leeming (9)
St Mark's CE Junior School, Salisbury

Party On The Moon

Come to my party on the moon,
Don't forget to bring your spoon,
Floating sandwiches and strawberry jelly,
I'm upside down on my belly,
Mars and the galaxy have just flown by,
There go my party bags, oh, I could cry,
Party games and big balloons,
Musical chairs on Neptune,
Time for home, but I'm far away,
It has been a happy birthday!

Nancy Neville (8)
St Mark's CE Junior School, Salisbury

A Stinky Shark

Deep in the water, where the ocean is dark,
There lived a stinky shark,
All the fish thought
That he was quite tangy,
But this only made him angry,
The dolphins were smart
And avoided his farts,
But the fish weren't so lucky,
He could wipe out millions
And would affect billions,
So here is one piece of advice...
Avoid the stink bombs!

Tilde Williams (8)

St Mark's CE Junior School, Salisbury

The Purple Turtle

On a beach there was
A purple turtle
And on that turtle
Were some cool shades.
On the deckchair was the turtle
And in his hand was a banana lolly,
The seagull came and took it away
And never came back again,
The turtle was sad,
With nothing to eat,
So crawled into his shell
And went to sleep!

Sophie Lee (8)
St Mark's CE Junior School, Salisbury

My White Unicorn

I have a white unicorn,
He looks lovely,
When he's in flight
Up in the sky
Ever so high
With bright rainbow stars
Flying by
And rainbow clouds
Whooshing by
My bright white unicorn's eyes.

Enya Harding (8)
St Mark's CE Junior School, Salisbury

Piddles

Mr Giraffe has a muddle,
With a puddle,
He is looking for Skittles
And that makes him piddle,
You see now, Skittles
Make him piddle!

Joey Larkham (7)
St Mark's CE Junior School, Salisbury

Sea Land

I saw an army
Of camouflaged mermaids
Out to make war,
I heard aggressive, giant lobsters
Footsteps running on the ground,
I heard the heartbeat,
Like an earthquake,
Of the sea dragon's heart.
I saw giant ships
That looked like sea creatures.

Joseph Ager (10)
Western CE Primary School, Winchester

My Favourite Adventure

One day, I got sucked into a cloud,
It was an amazing, fluffy, white cloud,
It took me higher and higher,
I got nervous,
Suddenly, it stopped,
It tipped me off at a different dimension,
This time, the grass wasn't lush green,
It was made of delicious strawberry laces,
I picked one up, it tasted delicious,
I spotted a wobbly footed gingerbread man,
One button was missing off his jacket,
Not that I cared,
Suddenly, astonishingly, carousel music floated in
the soft breeze,
Excited, I ran and jumped on it,
The red and white lollipops bounced up and down,
I squealed with delight,
Then I heard a talking, fluffy cloud,
After a while, I had to go,
I promised I'd come back,
So I did.

Charlotte Higgins (9)
Whitesheet Primary Academy, Zeals

War Of The Dragons

Sitting on a fire dragon,
Battling an ice dragon,
Flying through a coloured sky
Made of blue raspberry slushies,
Tasty clouds were made of cotton candy,
The ground was made of stinky blue cheese,
Lava flows like Fanta and tastes like water,
On the ice side, the ice was made of blueberries,
Snow was made of icing sugar,
One breathes fire and the other breathes snow,
The snow puts the fire out,
The fire melts the snow,
The battles ends with swimming in a lake,
They eat the sky and snack on the clouds.

Elliot Winter-White (7)

Whitesheet Primary Academy, Zeals

The Chleach

The Chleach was a creepy creature,
He had a human side and a leach side,
He had a pet pig, it was a flying pig,
The pig took Chleach on his back and *wham!*
They landed in a wasteland next to a volcano,
They saw a dinosaur,
He and his pet pig shuffled over to it,
The dinosaur licked his lips and roared,
Chleach's belly rumbled,
He jumped and latched on and started drinking.

Nathaniel Winter-White (9)
Whitesheet Primary Academy, Zeals

The Cat Who Loved Spaghetti

Spaghetti Cat dressed in a suit,
The table could move on its own,
The chair danced on Strictly,
Under the table, there was a rainbow,
It tasted like Skittles,
His whiskers twirled around when he had spaghetti
And his hat swirled around,
His suit comes off when he eats
Because it doesn't like stains,
He loves the letter 'S',
He is the spaghetti cat and he is amazing.

Ellie-May Manning (8)
Whitesheet Primary Academy, Zeals

Me, The Chair And My Dragon

My bedroom chair was not normal...

It loved fighting dragons,
So he was fighting my pet dragon,
I just stayed out of it
And ate a cotton candy cloud,
There were rats skittering around,
So I stood on the sofa,
Then the chair started coming for me,
So I jumped on my dragon and flew away
And grabbed a cloud on the way.

Fae Duggan (8)
Whitesheet Primary Academy, Zeals

Crazy Stuff!

Eating a rotten metal house
Made my teeth break.
My friend died from jumping over
Fifty thousand scary rattlesnakes.
My other friend died from doing backflips
Over a robotic pig and he broke his neck.
Jumping on cheeseburger trampolines,
Using chicken sticks as toothpicks
And elves eating the moon
Using a big fat spoon!

Stefan Pirvulescu (8)
Whitesheet Primary Academy, Zeals

My Pet Unicorn

I have a pet unicorn,
It looks like a sparkling rainbow
And when I take it to school,
My friends begin to cheer with joy,
'Cause when it goes to the bathroom...
Skittles pop out!

But when it's time to go home,
Everyone sighs,
I hop on its back to fly away
But when it flies,
Slime, slime, slime!

Summer Johnson (10)
Whitesheet Primary Academy, Zeals

The Chicken Dog!

My morning walk was a disaster...

The chicken dog is fluffy,
He loves burgers,
He is funny and happy,
He likes to run,
One day, the chicken dog went up to the moon
And ate it!
He ate so much, he got fat
And his tummy exploded
And chicken came out of his belly
And all his feathers went everywhere.

Albert Antony Ransome (8)
Whitesheet Primary Academy, Zeals

Underwater Castle

A ship went inside the castle,
The pirates all went,
There were a lot of soldiers long ago,
They all got killed,
By a shark who ate them
And the castle in one big go!

Elliot Hayes (8)
Whitesheet Primary Academy, Zeals

Practising Karate With The Queen

I went to London to see the Queen,
When I saw her, I started to scream,
We went to the hall
Not for a ball,
I did a kick or two on her bum,
She said, "Oww!"
But then she isn't just a queen,
She's a Karate Queen!
She said, "Hiya!"
I said, "Bye!" Then went home,
One thing I learnt not to do
Is karate with the Queen!

Katie Vollentine (9)
Wickham CE Primary School, Wickham

Colourful Wonderland

Roses are red,
Violets are blue,
Purple is nice
And yellow too.

I like to sing,
I like to dance,
I like to swing
High on a branch.

Colours are great,
Colours are cool,
I couldn't pick one
Because I like them all.

Strawberries are nice,
Raspberries too,
Give me a hug,
I love you.

Dogs are nice,
Dogs are cute,

Dogs are happy,
Just like you!

Summer Mullins (8)
Wickham CE Primary School, Wickham

The Enchanted Forest

The sun is glistening through
The summer-green trees,
The birds are tweeting
And there are no clouds in sight.
I feel the soft, soothing green grass
On my feet as I am walking.
The squirrels are scuttling
Up the hard, brown bark.
The deer are running like lightning
Because spring is finally here,
I feel happy because everyone is happy.

Poppy Lock (8)
Wickham CE Primary School, Wickham

The Balloon

I pop like a rock
Because I'm a maroon balloon,
I'm called Mia and my best friend is Lia,
Don't run away,
We want to play!
Happily today,
Dance away every day,
With brand new friends on the way!

Libby-Rose Fitzgerald (9)
Wickham CE Primary School, Wickham

My Imaginary World

In my imaginary world,
Money grows on trees,
Your favourite animals can talk,
Like meerkats, wolves and bees,
In my magical imaginary world,
Mythical animals are real, like dragons and
unicorns
And roses would not have sharp thorns,
You can fly by your colourful wings
And birds sing,
You have magical powers
And you can time travel and skip hours,
You can be in the best fairytale
And no one hurts the bugs and snails,
You can be a princess
And if you click your fingers there is no mess.

Oliver Barnes (10)
Wylye Valley CEVA Primary School, Codford

156

War Begins

There they walk into gory death,
Soldiers running in distress,
They're like lions facing their enemy,
Fighting furiously for the country,
Bang! The soldiers go down like dominoes,
Gas is dancing around, spreading fear,
Their feet are getting swallowed by mud,
In the trenches, soldiers are hiding tortoises,
The bullets are raining from the sky,
They're butterflies cocooning,
Waiting for the war to be over.

Poppy Barnes (10)
Wylye Valley CEVA Primary School, Codford

Underwater BBQ!

My underwater BBQ went terribly wrong...

The sauces floated away.
I didn't know if the lettuce was lettuce or seaweed.
An octopus stole my tongs.
Something ate all the meat
and the buns were soaked.
My kebabs were sandy.
I couldn't see what I was doing
as a squid was on my face!
The coal was damp
and I couldn't eat through my snorkel!

Margot Clarke (10)
Wylye Valley CEVA Primary School, Codford

Young Writers Information

We hope you have enjoyed reading this book – and that you will continue to in the coming years.

If you're a young writer who enjoys reading and creative writing, or the parent of an enthusiastic poet or story writer, do visit our website **www.youngwriters.co.uk**. Here you will find free competitions, workshops and games, as well as recommended reads, a poetry glossary and our blog. There's lots to keep budding writers motivated to write!

If you would like to order further copies of this book, or any of our other titles, then please give us a call or visit **www.youngwriters.co.uk**.

Young Writers
Remus House
Coltsfoot Drive
Peterborough
PE2 9BF
(01733) 890066
info@youngwriters.co.uk

Join in the conversation!
Tips, news, giveaways and much more!

 YoungWritersUK    @YoungWritersCW